Ladybird 🐞 Readers

MOOMIN

The Wish

Series Editor: Sorrel Pitts
Text adapted by Mary Taylor

LADYBIRD BOOKS

UK | USA | Canada | Ireland | Australia
India | New Zealand | South Africa

Ladybird Books is part of the Penguin Random House group of companies
whose addresses can be found at global.penguinrandomhouse.com.
www.penguin.co.uk   www.puffin.co.uk   www.ladybird.co.uk

Penguin
Random House
UK

Adapted from the story 'Moomin and the Wishing Star', first published by Puffin Books, 2015
This version published by Ladybird Books Ltd, 2019
001

Characters and artwork are the original creation of Tove Jansson
Text and illustrations copyright © Moomin Characters™, 2019
All rights reserved

Printed in China

A CIP catalogue record for this book is available from the British Library

ISBN: 978–0–241–36529–8

All correspondence to:
Ladybird Books
Penguin Random House Children's
80 Strand, London WC2R 0RL

MIX
Paper from
responsible sources
FSC® C018179

Ladybird Readers

MOOMIN

The Wish

Based on the original stories
by Tove Jansson

Picture words

Moomin

Moominmamma

Snufkin

Moominpappa

Sniff

Snorkmaiden

lake

pebble

star

shooting star

shine

sky

wish (noun)
make a wish (verb)

It was hot. Moomin found
a small lake. He wanted
to swim!

Then, he saw something
in the water. It was small
and white.

It was a beautiful
little pebble.

"Wow! It shines!"
thought Moomin.
"I must show it to
my family."

Moomin took his pebble home.

"Wow!" said Snorkmaiden. "The pebble shines. It's a beautiful star!"

"A star!" said Sniff. "Great! We can make a wish!"

"What is a wish?"
asked Moomin.

"We can ask for something
nice," said Sniff.

"Let's make a wish!"
Snorkmaiden said.

"Remember, you found it," Moominmamma said to Moomin. "It's your wish."

That night, Moomin
could not sleep.

"Is my pebble a star? Do I have
a wish? What is a good wish?
Something for me? Something
for my family? Oh dear!"

"I must ask Snufkin,"
he thought.

Moomin told Snufkin about
his problems.

"Look! The pebble isn't
shining now!"
said Moomin.

"We must take it back to
the lake," said Snufkin.

In the water, they could see the stars in the sky above.

"Put the pebble back in the lake, and make your wish," said Snufkin.

Moomin thought, but he
could not make a wish.

"Look at the sky!"
said Snufkin.
"Shooting stars!" said
Moomin. "I wish my
family was here."

"That's your wish!"
said Snufkin.

At breakfast, Moomin said,
"I made my wish!"

"What is it?" asked
Snorkmaiden.

"You must wait," smiled Moomin. "Moominmamma, can we have a picnic tonight?"

That night, they had a
picnic by the lake.

There were many stars
in the sky . . .

. . . but they could not see
any shooting stars.

Moomin was sad.

Then . . .

"Look! Shooting stars!"
said Snorkmaiden.

Moomin looked up at the stars, and he was happy. "That's my wish!" he thought.

"Your wish was for us to see shooting stars!" said Snorkmaiden. "Thank you!"

They all enjoyed Moomin's wish.

Activities

The key below describes the skills practiced in each activity.

 Spelling and writing

 Reading

 Speaking

 Critical thinking

 Preparation for the Cambridge Young Learners exams

1 Look and read. Put a ✓ or a ✗ in the boxes.

1 This is
   Moomin.   ✓

2 This is
   Snorkmaiden.   ☐

3 This is
   Moominpappa.   ☐

4 This is
   Snufkin.   ☐

5 This is
   Sniff.   ☐

Write the missing letters.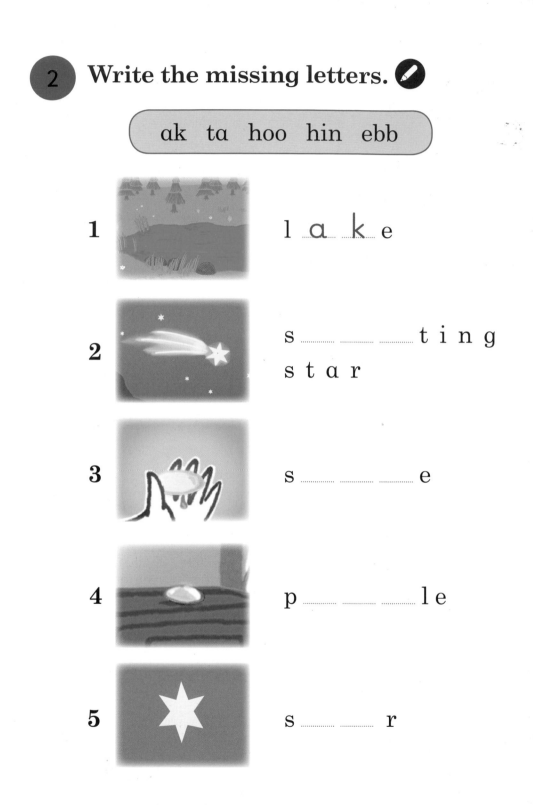

ak ta hoo hin ebb

1 l a k e

2 s _ _ _ t i n g
s t a r

3 s _ _ _ e

4 p _ _ _ l e

5 s _ _ r

3 Read the sentences and choose the correct answers.

1 It was
   a hot.
   b a hot.

2 Moomin wanted
   a to swim!
   b for swim!

3 Moomin . . . something in the water.
   a see
   b saw

4 It . . . small and white.
   a was
   b is

4 Do the crossword.

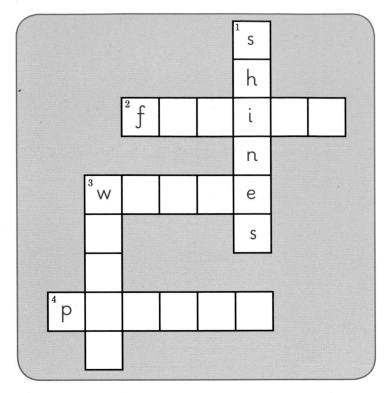

Across

2 Moomin wanted to show the pebble to his . . .

3 The pebble was small and . . .

4 The . . . was beautiful.

Down

1 "Wow! It . . . !" thought Moomin.

3 Moomin saw the pebble in the . . .

Moomin took his pebble home.

"Wow!" said Snorkmaiden. "The pebble shines. It's a beautiful star!"

"What is a wish?" asked Moomin.

"We can ask for something nice," said Sniff.

"A star!" said Sniff. "Great! We can make a wish!"

1 Moomin took the pebble

a home.

b to school.

2 "It's a beautiful . . . !" said Snorkmaiden.

a sun

b star

3 Sniff wanted to

a take the pebble home.

b make a wish.

4 What is a wish?

a Asking for something nice.

b Eating something nice.

6 **Find the words.**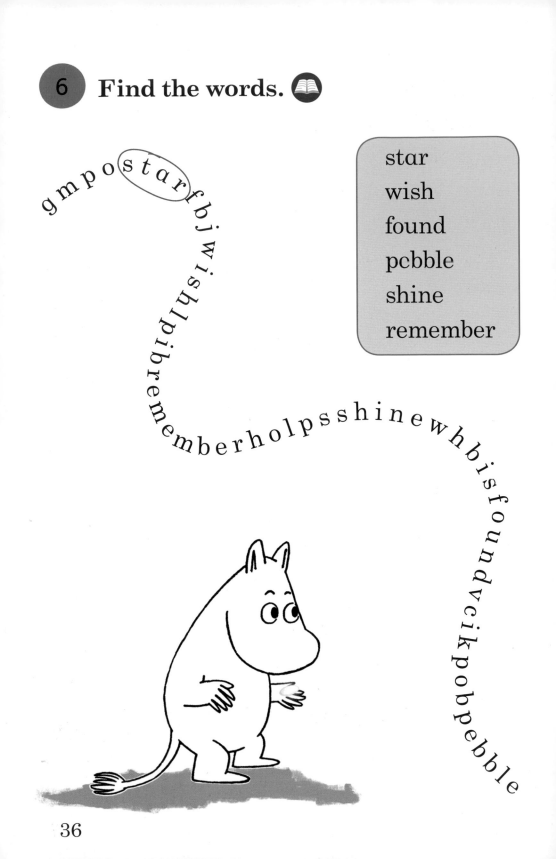

gmpo(starf)bjiwishlpidibrememberholpsshinewhbisfoundvcikpohpebble

star

wish

found

pcbble

shine

remember

7 **Ask and answer the questions with a friend.** 💬 ❓

1

> *What did Moomin find?*

> *He found a pebble.*

2 "It's a beautiful star,"
said Snorkmaiden.
Why did she think this?

3 What did Sniff want to do?

4 "Remember, it's your wish,"
said Moominmamma.
Why did she say this?

5 What is your wish?

Write the correct past-tense verbs.

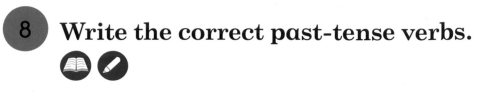

1 That night, Moomin (**cannot**)
…could not… sleep.

2 He (**do not**) …………………… know what
wish to make.

3 He (**go**) …………………… to find Snufkin
and ask him.

4 Moomin (**tell**) …………………… Snufkin
about his problems.

9 **Look at the letters. Write the words.**

1 (g i n h s i n)

The pebble wasn't ..... shining ..... now.

2 (k e a l)

"We must take the pebble back
to the ...."

3 (r t a w e)

In the ...., they could see
the stars in the sky above.

4 (b p l e b e)

Moomin put his .... back
in the lake.

Look and read. Write *yes* or *no*.

"Look at the sky!" said Snufkin.
"Shooting stars!" said Moomin. "I wish my family was here."

"That's your wish!" said Snufkin.

1 Moomin is looking at the sky.　　yes

2 Moomin can see shooting stars.

3 Snufkin is behind the lake.

4 Moomin is in front of the lake.

5 Moomin does not wish his family was there.

11 **Circle the correct words.**

1 At (**breakfast**), / **dinner**, Moomin said, "I made my wish!"

2 That night, they had a picnic by the **house**. / **lake**.

3 There were many stars in the **lake**. / **sky**.

4 But they could not see any shooting **stars**. / **star**.

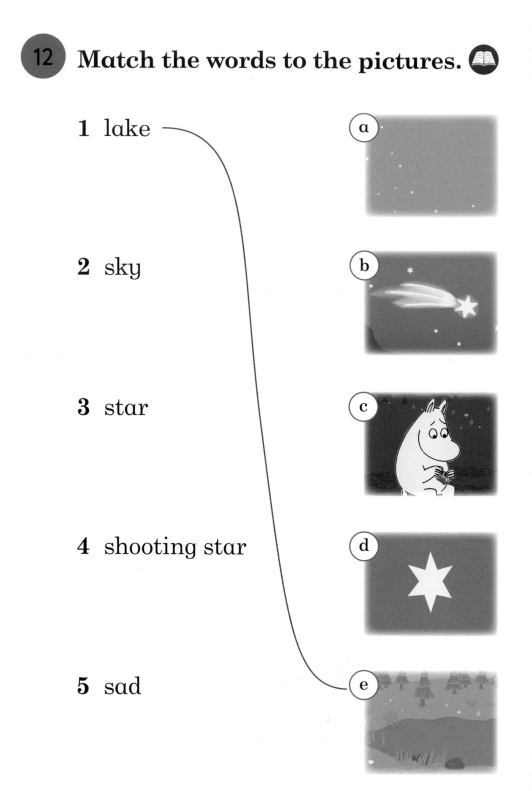

12 **Match the words to the pictures.**

1 lake

2 sky

3 star

4 shooting star

5 sad

a

b

c

d

e

13 **Order the sentences. Write 1—5.** 📖

.... Snorkmaiden said, "Thank you!" for Moomin's wish.

.... Moomin looked up at the stars, and he was happy.

.... They all enjoyed Moomin's wish.

....1.... Snorkmaiden saw shooting stars.

.... Moomin thought, "That's my wish!"

14 **Find the words.**

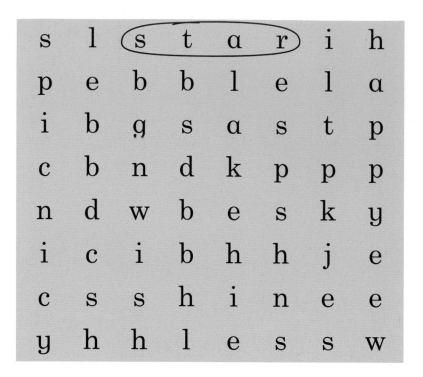

s	l	s	t	a	r	i	h
p	e	b	b	l	e	l	a
i	b	g	s	a	s	t	p
c	b	n	d	k	p	p	p
n	d	w	b	e	s	k	y
i	c	i	b	h	h	j	e
c	s	s	h	i	n	e	e
y	h	h	l	e	s	s	w

star

sky

shine

pebble

wish

happy

lake

picnic

15 Who said this?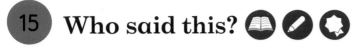

Moomin   Snorkmaiden

1 "The pebble shines. It's a beautiful star!"

said ..Snorkmaiden...

2 "What is a wish?"

asked ....

3 "I made my wish!"

said ....

4 "Your wish was for us to see shooting stars!"

said ....

16 **Circle the best answers.** 📖 ✿ ❓

1 Why could Moomin not sleep?

   a Because he did not know what wish to make.

   b Because he wanted to see a shooting star.

2 Why did Moomin put his pebble back in the lake?

   a Because he did not want the pebble.

   b Because the pebble stopped shining.

3 What was Moomin's wish?

   a He wanted his family and friends to see shooting stars.

   b He wanted to have a picnic by the lake.

17 **Ask and answer the questions with a friend.** 💬 ❓

1

> *What is a wish?*

> *Asking for something nice.*

2 Do you make wishes?

3 When do you make them?

4 How do you make them?

The Gingerbread Man	Sly Fox and Red Hen	The Monster Next Door	Little Red Riding Hood	Superhero Max
978-0-241-25442-4	978-0-241-25443-1	978-0-241-25444-8	978-0-241-25446-2	978-0-241-28368-4
The Magic Paintbrush	We Can Help!	Wild Animals	Dinosaurs	Great Trains
978-0-241-35822-1	978-0-241-28367-7	978-0-241-25445-5	978-0-241-25447-9	978-0-241-29808-4
Peter Rabbit Goes to the Treehouse	Peter Rabbit and the Angry Owl	The Peter Rabbit Club	Sports Day	Going on a Picnic
978-0-241-25449-3	978-0-241-28369-1	978-0-241-29811-4	978-0-241-26222-1	978-0-241-26221-4
Daddy Pig's New Van	School Trip	Daddy Pig's Office	In a Plane	Playing Football
978-0-241-28371-4	978-0-241-28372-1	978-0-241-29814-5	978-0-241-31945-1	978-0-241-31947-5
Spring is Here!	Topsy and Tim The Big Race	Pom Pom the Winner	The Wish	Grimlock Stops the Decepticons
978-0-241-29809-1	978-0-241-25448-6	978-0-241-35820-7	978-0-241-36529-8	978-0-241-31954-3
Hungry Animals	Mountains	Big and Small		
978-0-241-29844-2	978-0-241-31948-2	978-0-241-35818-4		

Now you're ready for Level 3 !